Walt Disney's

Donald Duck
AND
Gyro Gearloose

D1245122

WALT DISNEY PUBLICATIONS, INC.
BURBANK, CALIFORNIA

Michael Lynton—Vice President, Marketing, Publications   Randy Achee—Publisher
Len Wein—Editor-in-Chief   Bob Foster—Editor   Sally Prendergast—Marketing Manager
Andrea Beam—National Sales Manager   Barbara Pietuch—Production Manager

THE GREATEST INVENTOR OF THEM ALL

Gyro Gearloose was created in 1951, when Carl Barks needed a screwy inventor to put across a gag in a Donald Duck story. To make the character look zany, Barks gave him baggy clothes, large clownish feet, and a wild mop of hair. Beyond that he wasted little thought on Gyro, who was incidental to the plot at hand. The inventor came onstage riding a pogo stick, spoke three lines about trying to churn butter by hopping up and down, and made a quick exit. The whole scene lasted five panels and could as easily have been a swan song as a debut.

Yet Gyro was back the following month, this time as the creator of "think boxes," machines to make animals talk and act like human beings. Once again, Barks concentrated more on plot than on character, spinning an elaborate satire of comic book reality in which Disney's talking ducks are suddenly confronted with **real** animals that behave like human beings. At the same time, by using Gyro to set up this spoof, Barks was able to round out the inventor's character and establish a pattern for future tales. From now on, Gyro would be a scientist rather than a mere crackpot. Strong technical skills would help him bring his wild fantasies to life in ways that could be funny, unsettling, or even disasterous for Donald and his nephews. In short, Gyro became an extension of Bark's own creative power. The artist's think boxes were nothing more nor less than the rectangular panels which focused his stories and held them in place on the page, boxes in which ducks think and act like humans.

To balance such awesome power, Barks gave Gyro a dreamy, almost deadpan personality that puts him vaguely out of step with the very reality he seeks to shape and control. As the think-box story reaches its crisis, the inventor stares blankly into space, reeling off technical mumbo jumbo as if recalling a recipe for brownies; while in the tale of the educated worms, he remains completely unaware of the havoc his science has wrought at Mudhen Lake. In every story there seems to be one detail so small or so obvious that Gyro overlooks it, and he often ends up wondering what went wrong. In the tale of the red dye, a confusion of addresses causes all the trouble; in "The Madcap Mariner," the inventor's own weak stomach kayos him. These failings and miscalculations allow Barks to stay one step ahead of his character, manipulating the manipulator and pointing up morals for his reader.

Donald's role in the stories is that of scoffer or sorcerer's apprentice: the man who believes too little or too much. In either case, the operative word is **too**. Like Gyro, Donald is a creature of extremes who loses sight of vital details, such as the structural absurdity of fastening a boat together with railroad spikes. Only Barks keeps everything in perspective for us, both graphically and philosophically. His lessons take many forms, but one line sums them all up neatly: "Nobody can make a machine so **smart** that some jerk won't be too **dumb** to run it!"

—Giles Moran

Creator Credits

Front cover by Daan Jippes.

"The Think Boxes," written and drawn by Carl Barks (first published in WDC&S 141, 1952).

"Educated Worms," written and drawn by Carl Barks (first published in WDC&S 153, 1953).

"The Day Duckburg Got Dyed," written and drawn by Carl Barks (first published in WDC&S 201, 1957).

"The Mad Cap Mariner," written and drawn by Carl Barks (first published in WDC&S 247, 1961).

"Brain Strain," art by Carl Barks, author unknown (first published in Gyro Gearloose one-shot 1184, 1961).

ISBN 1-56115-021-5

Disney Comics Album #1—Walt Disney's Donald Duck and Gyro Gearloose—published by W. D. Publications, Inc., a subsidiary of The Walt Disney Company, 500 South Buena Vista Street, Burbank, California 91521. Entire contents © The Walt Disney Company. All rights reserved. Nothing herein contained may be reproduced without written permission of The Walt Disney Company, Burbank, California.

1 3 5 7 9 8 6 4 2

YOU CALLED THOSE CRATES **THINK BOXES**! WOULD I BE TOO INQUISITIVE IF I ASKED —

CERTAINLY NOT, DONALD! I'M PROUD OF THESE BOXES! THEY'RE MY NEWEST AND **GREATEST** INVENTION!

THEY'RE FULL OF GADGETS THAT SEND ELECTRIC THOUGHT RAYS, UNCA DONALD!

SEE! WE PUT ONE ON EACH SIDE OF AN ANIMAL TRAIL, AND ANY ANIMALS THAT PASS THROUGH THE RAY BEAM LEARN HOW TO **THINK**!

AND, MORE THAN THAT, UNCA DONALD, THE ANIMALS WILL BE ABLE TO **TALK** AND **DO THINGS LIKE HUMAN BEINGS**!

NOW I'LL TURN ON THE THOUGHT RAY, AND TOMORROW MORNING WE'LL COME BACK AND SEE IF IT HAS WORKED!

(WHEET!) WHEW! AND I THOUGHT THAT BAGGAGE BUGGY WAS A **SCREWY** INVENTION!

HEY! HOW COME YOU KIDS ARE MIXED UP IN THIS **NONSENSE**?

WE'RE **WORKING** FOR MR. GEARLOOSE!

WE'RE HIS **ASSISTANTS**!

OH, THAT THE NAME OF **DUCK** SHOULD EVER SINK SO LOW!

THAT EVENING!

BOYS, YOU HAVE TO STOP WORKING FOR THAT SCREWBALL, GYRO!

WHY, UNCA DONALD?

YOU—YOU—WELL, YOU'LL BE THE LAUGHINGSTOCK OF THE TOWN! YOU'LL BE JOKES!

OH!

THINK OF IT! PEOPLE WILL HEAR ABOUT YOU HELPING GYRO WITH HIS THINK BOXES, AND THEY'LL TEASE YOU FOR THE REST OF YOUR LIVES!

WE'LL TAKE OUR CHANCES!

PEOPLE SOON STOPPED TEASING EDISON AND MARCONI!

BUT GYRO'S NO EDISON! HE'S JUST A HARMLESS CRACKPOT!

SO WAS EDISON UNTIL HIS INVENTIONS CLICKED!

I SEE THE KIDS HAVE TO BE STRAIGHTENED OUT! THEY'RE COMPLETELY SOLD ON THAT WACKY-BRAIN'S IDEAS!

I'LL USE STRATEGY! I'LL MAKE 'EM SO ASHAMED OF HIM, THEY'LL QUIT!

BUT, NEVER MIND! IF YOU'RE GOING TO SAVE YOUR UNCLE, YOU BETTER START HOPPING! THEY WENT THAT-A-WAY!

UNCA DONALD WOULD GET MIXED UP IN THIS!

UNCA DONALD! UNCA DONALD!

WHAT WOULD A WOLF WANT WITH HIM, ANYWAY?

UH, OH!

YESSIR! I SUDDENLY GOT THE DOGGONEDEST CRAVING FOR ROAST DUCK!

WE CAN'T TACKLE THAT WOLF WITH OUR BARE HANDS! WE'VE GOT TO GET GYRO TO HELP US!

GYRO! GYRO! MR. GEARLOOSE! CAN YOU REVERSE THOSE THINK BOXES —

MAKE 'EM UNSMART A WOLF?

WHY, YES! I CAN DOUBLE THE BEAM BACK FROM 'B' BOX TO 'A' BOX, CAUSING THE POLAR NEGATIVE TO BREAK UP THE COSMIC POSITIVE —

NEVER MIND THE DETAILS! WE'VE GOT TO BREAK UP A DINNER DATE!

OLD BOMBASTRO, GRANDFATHER OF ALL THE LAKE'S BASS, STRIKES!

GLOM!

UH, OH! LOOKS LIKE TROUBLE OUT THERE!

SNORT! GROWL!

THE FISH IS TOO MUCH FOR THE WORMS! THEY CAN'T HOLD HIM!

I'LL HAVE TO GET MORE WORMS FROM GYRO! THAT FISH WILL WIN ME THE PRIZE!

ALL RIGHT, DONALD! TAKE A WHOLE BUCKETFUL! BUT BE CAREFUL! IT'S DANGEROUS TO USE MORE THAN A DOZEN AT A TIME!

HA! DANGEROUS, HE SAYS! HOW COULD THESE DINKY LITTLE WORMS BE DANGEROUS?

DONALD IS SOON TO LEARN!

YIPPEE! AT LEAST FIFTY WORMS ARE HAULING IN OLD BOMBASTRO!

GO AHEAD AND GET TOUGH! I STILL **WIN** THE DERBY! I CAUGHT OLD BOMBASTRO!

YOU'RE DISQUALIFIED! YOU DIDN'T CATCH BOMBASTRO—YOUR **WORMS** DID!

AT THAT MOMENT GYRO GEARLOOSE WANDERS INTO THE SCENE!

WHAT GOES?...SOMEBODY MAD AT SOMEBODY?

YES! THE FISHERMEN ARE MAD AT UNCA DONALD BECAUSE HIS WORMS GOT OUT OF CONTROL!

HAW! DON'T LET THAT WORRY YOU, GENTLEMEN! THE WORMS ONLY LIVE **TWELVE HOURS!**

ACCORDING TO MY WATCH, THEY SHOULD ALL EXPIRE IN FIVE MINUTES!

BUT THAT'S NO **CALAMITY!** IF ANY OF YOU BOYS WANT **MORE** WORMS, I'LL HAVE A NEW BATCH HATCHED OFF AT DAYLIGHT TOMORROW!

NOW, WHAT DID I SAY THAT MAKES EVERYBODY MAD AT ME?

Walt Disney's **Donald Duck** *The* MADCAP MARINER

DUCKS ARE PAWNS AND COD ARE KINGS IN THIS BRINY TALE OF ICE AND FISH IN THE ROARING NORTHERN SEAS!

OLD SALTS SAY THERE'S NO FAIRER SIGHT ON THE SEAS THAN A COD FISHING SCHOONER WITH ALL HER LINEN HUNG!

BUT WE NEED MORE *SPEED*! SPLICE OUT THE MIZZEN HALYARDS! SPLICE ON THE POOPSAIL SPANKERS! CRACK

DIP HER RAILS AND WET HER GALLEY STACK! WE'RE GOING TO BE *FIRST* TO THE DAVIS STRAIT IF WE HAVE TO PUSH THE *DAFFY-O* THERE IN FROG SUITS!

UNCLE SCROOGE SAYS THE *DAFFY-O* *HAS TO* WIN THE FISHERMEN'S GOLD CUP THIS YEAR OR *ELSE*!

WHICH MEANS WE MUST BEAT THE FISHING FLEET BACK TO PORT WITH A FULL LOAD OF COD IN THE HOLD!

UNCA SCROOGE IS THE ONLY SCHOONER OWNER WHO HASN'T WON THE GOLD CUP AT LEAST ONCE, AND IT'S BEGINNING TO HURT!

IT'S ODD, THOUGH, THAT HE'D PUT A GREEN HAND LIKE UNCA DONALD IN CHARGE OF THE SHIP!

UNCA SCROOGE IS TRYING SOMETHING *DIFFERENT!* EVERY YEAR HE HAS FAILED WITH THE *BEST* CAPTAINS AND CREWS HIS MONEY COULD HIRE!

THIS YEAR HE'S SENDING THE *DAFFY-O* TO THE FISHING GROUNDS WITH A *LUBBER* CREW AND A CAPTAIN THAT CAN'T COUNT THE MASTS!

AND SOME MYSTERIOUS *SECRET DEVICE* WHICH HE THINKS IS GOING TO CATCH *MORE* CODFISH THAN ANYTHING BEFORE OR SINCE!

SECRET DEVICE

KEEP OUT!

THERE'S A SHIP CROWDING US! MAYBE IT'S A *SPY!* HELM YOUR STARBOARD!

WHATEVER THAT ORDER MEANT, THE HELMSMAN STEERED TO *PORTSIDE!*

LUCKY FOR US HE DID! UNCA DONALD'S ORDERS WOULD HAVE *ROLLED THE SHIP OVER!*

NIGHT FALLS!

DO YOU KIDS SUPPOSE WE HAVE COME A HUNDRED MILES FROM SHORE?

THAT DEPENDS ON HOW MANY TIMES YOU'VE CHANGED COURSE, UNCA DONALD!

WAK! I'VE CHANGED ONCE TOO OFTEN! WE'RE SAILING UP THE STREETS OF A *CITY!*

CAPTAIN, WE'RE HEADED STRAIGHT FOR A *HOLE* IN A BIG ICEBERG! WHAT SHALL WE DO?

DO? *SAIL THROUGH THE HOLE*, YOU BLINKIN' SWABS!

YOU'D BETTER DO IT, CAPTAIN! THE HOLE IS ONLY BIG ENOUGH FOR A *ROWBOAT*!

I'LL BE KEELHAULED!

HEAVE BACK ON THE GAFFLE BRACES! LOWER THE BINNACLES! TAKE IN THE WASHING!

I MEAN *MAKE A U-TURN*!

SNAP

CRACK

BAM

DID WE HIT THE BERG?

NO, BUT I BET WE'RE THE FIRST SCHOONER THAT EVER SAILED INTO DAVIS STRAIT *BACKWARD*!

LATER...

BUT LASH ME TO A YARDARM! HE *IS* CATCHING FISH!

IT MUST BE THE *TONE* OF THAT BELL!

OUSE →

THOSE FISH *DO* SEEM TO WANT AN EDUCATION, GYRO!

WHAT WILL THEY *LEARN* IN YOUR SCHOOL?

HEH! THAT ONE SHOULDN'T TRUST *EVERY* GUY IN A MORTARBOARD HAT!

AVAST, GYRO! LAY OFF! CLOSE YOUR CODFISH COLLEGE! ONE MORE FINNY STUDENT WILL *SINK THE SHIP!*

AND SO —

MR. McDUCK, YOUR SHIP HAS JUST BROKEN ALL RECORDS FOR CATCHING COD! CAN YOU TELL US SOMETHING OF HOW THIS WAS ACCOMPLISHED?

I DAREN'T SPILL THE BEANS ABOUT MY *SECRET DEVICE,* DONALD! WHAT SHALL I TELL THEM?

LEAVE IT TO ME, UNCLE SCROOGE!

I DID IT, LADIES AND GENTLEMEN! *I,* WITH MY EXPERT SEAMANSHIP, MY UNCANNY KNOWLEDGE OF CODFISH —

AVAST WITH THOSE FLASHES, PHOTOGS! WE OLD SALTS FROM GLOUCESTER MUST KEEP OUR EYES SHARP FOR GOOD SPOTS TO TOSS OUT A LINE!

POOF

THAT EXPLOSION WAS ALL POOF AND NO NOISE! IT DIDN'T GET A NOD FROM THE PLANE!

THE PILOTS COULDN'T HEAR IT, AND THE CLOUD OF BIRDS KEPT THEM FROM SEEING THE SMOKE! (SIGH!)

A FINE INVENTOR, YOU ARE! A REAL DUD— LIKE YOUR GUNPOWDER!

I MUST TRY A DIFFERENT WAY TO USE THE POWDER!

HMM! CERTAINLY A LOT OF FEATHERS ABOUT!

I DON'T WONDER! HALF OF MINE WERE BLOWN OFF!

YOU BUG ME! I'M ABOUT TO BLOW MY TOP!

BLOW YOUR TOP! ... DONALD! YOU'VE STARTED THE WHEELS OF INVENTION SPINNING!

THIS EXTINCT VOLCANO IS JUST THE RIGHT SIZE!

RIGHT SIZE FOR WHAT?

YOU'LL SEE! GATHER UP ALL THE FEATHERS YOU CAN FIND!

NOTHING DOING, YOU FEATHER-BRAINED TINKERER!

I ALMOST GOT BLOWN UP HELPING YOU WITH YOUR LAST FABULOUS INVENTION!

DONALD!

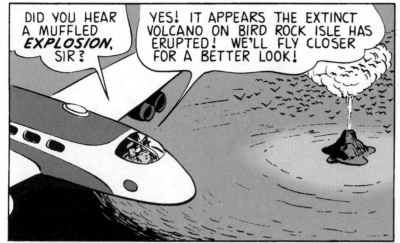